OOKIE
The Walrus Who Likes People

OOKIE

By
WILLIAM BRIDGES
Curator of Publications

New York Zoological Society

WILLIAM MORROW & COMPANY

THE WALRUS
WHO LIKES PEOPLE

With many photographic illustrations by
EMMY HAAS
and a few additional ones by
SAM DUNTON
Staff Photographer, New York Zoological Society

NEW YORK, 1962

By the Same Author

FOREWORD

All animals are interesting. Only a few are lovable. Just why some individual animals have an instant and abiding appeal for human beings, while others of the same species are — well, just interesting — is something I can't explain. I have known a couple of elephants and one wart hog and two alligators that had a special appeal to a lot of people, and any number of elephants and wart hogs and alligators that left those same people unmoved.

Ookie, the young Pacific walrus at the New York Aquarium, really does like people, and her liking has been reciprocated by thousands of visitors. As for the staff and the keepers — they adore her. She can do no wrong. Anything she does (and as the years go on it is safe to predict that she will become a spoiled problem walrus) is all right.

Among her human friends, she has no warmer admirers than Dr. Carleton Ray, who lifted her into an Eskimo boat off the coast of Alaska, and Dr. James W. Atz, who has written endlessly about her in the New York Zoological

Society's magazine, *Animal Kingdom,* and Charley Young, who has the daily care of her.

They, of course, are professionally concerned with Ookie's career. But she has captured many hearts among the visitors to the Aquarium, and none more devoted than Miss Emmy Haas, a skilled, ingenious, and ever-patient amateur photographer, whose studies of Ookie have been reproduced on two continents. She will, I think, go on photographing Ookie until the stores run out of film. Sam Dunton, the New York Zoological Society's own pet photographer, happened to be at the Aquarium on assignment at the time Ookie was climbing walls, and his series of pictures is reproduced on pages 19 to 24. All the rest are the work of Miss Haas's loving camera.

W. B.

OOKIE
The Walrus Who Likes People

Ookie is a walrus who likes people.

Maybe *all* baby walruses like people. Maybe, up in Alaska and Greenland and all through the icy waters around the North Pole, there are baby walruses who would just love to make friends with people. But mostly they don't get a chance. Up there in the frozen northland there is very little to eat, and the Eskimos have to hunt walruses and seals in order to live. To them, a baby walrus is just another animal, whose flesh is good to eat and whose skin will make them lengths of walrus-hide rope.

But Ookie was lucky. One morning, when she was only a few weeks old, she was swimming among the floating ice fields, when a boat, made of tightly stretched walrus skin, came skimming through the open water. Before she knew what was happening, she had been lifted into the boat. The Eskimos in the boat were hunting walruses for their winter's food supply. Usually they wouldn't have bothered to stop and capture a tiny 130-pound baby, as long as they had a chance to shoot its 3500-pound father or its 2500-pound mother. But this was a special hunting party. There was a man from the New York Aquarium in the boat, and he wanted a baby walrus —one like Ookie—to take back to New York. He was the one who made the Eskimos stop and pick her up.

Stan Wayman—courtesy *Life* Magazine, copyright 1958, Time Inc.

At first she was frightened. She kept calling "Ook-ook-ook-ook-ook," but after a while she did what any sensible baby walrus would do. She went to sleep. She curled her flippers under her body, rested her whiskery chin on the knees of the man from the Aquarium, and closed her eyes. Every now and then she woke up for a moment, long enough to say "Ook-ook-ook," and then she went back to sleep.

Once she shivered a little, for the wind was cold and biting, and the man found a piece of old, dry sack and spread it over her body. She woke up again and said, "Ook-ook."

"You know," said the man, "you ought to have a name. I can't just call you 'it' or 'you' or 'the baby walrus.' Now what shall I name you?"

The baby walrus rubbed her whiskers on the man's knees and snuggled down under the warm sack. "Ook-ook," she said.

"Ookie! That's it! And whenever I call you, you can answer me with your name. O.K., Ookie?"

Ookie said "Ook-ook" again, for to tell the truth, that was about the only thing a baby walrus *could* say. She didn't care what the man called her; she had never heard people talking before and didn't know what words meant. A long time afterward she did learn her name, and she would come swimming across her pool when she was called, but out there in the boat she only knew that the man was making friendly noises and wasn't going to hurt her. She was sleepy and not afraid.

The only thing was, she was just a little bit hungry. But that was all right, too, for after a while the boat came to the shore. The man lifted her out and put her on a sled, and then a great many laughing Eskimo children came and pulled the sled over the snow to their village. They all talked to her and called her by her new name. Meanwhile, the man poured some thick cream and some chopped-up clams into a little machine, which made a whirring sound, and before Ookie was more than half-awake he was offering her a whole big bottle of cream-and-clams. It tasted so good that Ookie drank it all, and then a second bottle too. After that, of course, she went to sleep again.

Ookie lived for many days in the Eskimo village in Alaska. Finally a great airplane came and she was put inside it. There was a lot of noise, and two days later the man carried her out of the airplane and put her in a truck. It made a different kind of noise, but the man sat beside her and patted her head. After a while he lifted her once more, and carried her to the edge of a big pool of clear, cold, sparkling salt water in the New York Aquarium.

"Well," he said, "this is your new home. Have fun, Ookie." And Ookie did.

Since this is a real story about the things that happened to Ookie after she came to live in the Aquarium, all the bad things have to be told about her as well as the good ones. The worst thing was that Ookie was pretty badly spoiled, especially about eating.

Everything went along quite well at first. The people at the Aquarium knew that baby walruses have to have very rich food, and so they made a kind of soup out of cream and chopped-up clams and vitamins. Ookie liked it. She always shut her eyes and almost swallowed the nursing bottle in her eagerness to drink. She could empty an eight-ounce baby bottle in fifteen seconds! And she never seemed to get enough. Almost as soon as she had finished one feeding, she would cry, "Ook-ook-ook-ook," to say that she wanted more. The Aquarium people had to feed her four times a

Stan Wayman—courtesy *Life* Magazine, copyright 1958, Time Inc.

day, and each day she drank almost three gallons of cream and clam juice and vitamins. It was no wonder that she gained more than a pound every day.

Finally they began putting her formula in a bucket, with a rubber nipple at the bottom of it, and that made the feeding go a little faster. But at last the time came when Ookie was old enough to be weaned, as every baby has to be.

Ookie didn't want to be weaned. She liked people, and she liked to have her keeper hold the bucket and talk to her while she drank her breakfast, her lunch, her dinner, and her in-between meals.

But one day the keeper simply poured Ookie's breakfast in a pan and put it in front of her. She sniffed at it and dipped the ends of her whiskers in it, but she wouldn't drink.

The Aquarium people were very stern with her. "Look, Ookie," they said. "You're getting to be a big baby walrus. You have to learn to eat by yourself. We'll just leave that pan in front of you until you do."

All day Ookie cried "Ook-ook-ook-ook" in the most pitiful way. She'd sniff at the pan, and cry, "Ook-ook," and then go swimming. Then she'd come back and sniff at the pan again, and cry "Ook-ook" some more.

She didn't eat anything all that day. But she was so fat that the Aquarium people knew it didn't really make any difference, so they let her alone. As you might expect, the next morning Ookie was really hungry, and the instant the pan of fresh cream and clam juice and vitamins was set in front of her, she dipped her whole face in it and began to drink by herself. She got cream and clams all over her whiskers, and she looked simply awful. But she had learned to eat by herself, and that was all that mattered. Afterward she went swimming and washed the cream off her face. That's one of the most convenient things about being a baby walrus. You can always go swimming and get clean.

The next worst thing that Ookie did—or maybe it was really the worst—was to run away from home.

It wasn't that she didn't like her home, for she did. She lived in a very large pool of cold salt water in the yard of the Aquarium, and it was deep enough for her to dive or swim on her back or do anything else. But she was always getting lonesome.

17

Many times each day her favorite keeper, whose name was Charley, came to the pool and talked to her. Sometimes he even put on a bathing suit and got into the water with her. Ookie could swim faster than Charley could, and she liked to dive under him and bump him in the stomach with her whiskers. When he got tired, he sat on the cement platform at the edge of the pool and Ookie rested her chin on his knees and went to sleep.

But Charley had many other things to do, and he couldn't be with Ookie *all* the time. That was why she got lonesome.

Now it happened that Ookie's pool was part of a clover-leaf-shaped set of three pools. Some penguins lived in the pool on one side, and several little harbor seals in the one on the other side. Each of the three pools was separated from the others by a wall thirty-seven inches high.

At first, when Ookie felt lonesome, she just stood up on her hind flippers and looked over the walls, first on one side and then on the other. The penguin pool didn't interest her much, for these penguins came from down around the South Pole, and Ookie had never seen one before. Besides, they were birds and didn't seem to be the sort of creatures it would be fun to play with.

But the seal pool simply fascinated Ookie. She stood for long minutes watching the seals chase each other through the water, rolling and diving, twisting and turning. They could swim as easily and as fast as Ookie herself. *They* were the kind of playmates she wanted

when she felt lonesome. And there was nothing but that thirty-seven-inch wall to keep her from joining them. . . .

The Aquarium people didn't see her the first time she ran away from home and went visiting in the seal pool. It happened just about dark one evening. One of the men at the Aquarium was eating his dinner in the restaurant, when he heard people shouting and laughing. He knew that something unexpected had happened, so he left his dinner and ran out of the restaurant to see what it was.

It was Ookie. She was in the seal pool, swimming in wide, lazy circles, trying to catch the seals. Of course, the seals couldn't imagine what this big animal was, for they hadn't been able to look over *their* wall and see Ookie. They were scared. Maybe they thought Ookie wanted to eat them. Actually, she just wanted to play.

The Aquarium man was almost as scared as the seals were. He was afraid that if Ookie did catch up with one of the seals, it might be so frightened that it would bite her and hurt her.

He quickly called some more men, and they opened the gate between the seal pool and Ookie's pool. Then they pushed her and pulled her until they got her back home.

The Aquarium man went back to his dinner. He was just getting ready to eat his dessert of apple pie and ice cream, when he heard the people laughing again.

Ookie was back in the seal pool.

So again they pushed her and pulled her and got her back home. And then again she climbed the wall and got in with the seals. Again and again and again!

By midnight the Aquarium people were just about worn out. Ookie was having such fun and was enjoying the pushing and the pulling so much, that she could have gone on climbing the wall all night. But at midnight her friends decided they'd keep her at home for a little while, anyway. They got a lot of boards and nailed them to the top of the wall, so high that Ookie couldn't possibly climb out. Then they went home and got a good night's sleep.

The next morning they took the boards down, for they weren't painted and didn't look nice. They knew Ookie would climb over again, so they waited and watched to see how she did it.

First she stood on tiptoe, with her hind flippers spread out like feet. When she did this, she was tall enough to hook her front flippers over the top of the wall.

Next, she lifted one hind flipper and then the other, and stood on the little cement ledge beside the wall, about a foot above the floor. That was easy for her to do, because she just pulled herself up with her front flippers as if they were arms.

From there on, it was even easier. Ookie rested all her weight on her front flippers and lifted the lower part of her body up the wall. After that she simply toppled over, landing on her head and neck on the other side.

It might hurt some animals to fall even three feet on their

head and neck, but not Ookie. She was so fat that it didn't hurt her a bit.

Once the Aquarium people saw exactly how Ookie climbed the wall, they had to get a carpenter and his helper to come and build it higher.

They built it forty-nine inches high, and Ookie climbed over it.

They built it fifty-seven inches high, and Ookie still climbed over.

They built it sixty-six inches high, which is almost as tall as a man, but Ookie kept right on climbing over it.

Ookie was having more fun than she had ever had in her life. The carpenters

had to come every day to build the wall higher, and the keepers had to be there while the carpenters were working, and of course the keepers talked to her and played with her, so she wouldn't get in the way. Ookie seemed to have an idea that each time the wall was built higher, her keeper friends *wanted*

her to climb over it, so that they could play with her. So she did.

But it wasn't fun for the Aquarium people. They were getting worried about something else. They were afraid Ookie would climb to the top of the very high wall while they weren't looking, and maybe fall so far that she would really hurt herself.

So at last they called the carpenter for the last time. "Build us a wall," they said, "that Ookie can't possibly climb over."

"And how high do you think that would be?"

The Aquarium people thought for a long time. They knew that as long as Ookie could stand on tiptoe and get her front flippers over the top of the wall, she could pull herself up and over. The only thing to do was to build a wall so high that she couldn't reach the top.

"Seven feet," they said. "Make the wall seven feet high."

Seven feet is a good deal taller than a man. And the Aquarium people were right — Ookie couldn't reach the top of it. She couldn't even see over it by standing on her hind flippers and stretching as far as possible.

For several days Ookie couldn't believe that her climbing fun was over. She stood on her rear flippers, braced her front flippers against the seven-foot wall, and looked up at the top, so high above her head. But she couldn't climb it, so after that she *had* to stay home.

But the wall no longer mattered. Her friends in the Aquarium had found an exciting new toy for her— a big plastic ball. Ookie was always easily pleased by anything new, and since she wasn't allowed to play with the seals, she was happy to play with the ball. In some ways it was even better than the seals, for it wouldn't swim away from her or be frightened or bite her. She could do all sorts of things with it that she couldn't have done with the seals. Sometimes she lay on her back on the floor of her haul-out (a place something like a beach, at the edge of her pool) and experimented with different ways of holding the ball. Her front flippers were big and strong and almost as useful as hands. Very soon she learned that she could hold the ball with only one flipper if she pressed it against her whiskers.

But it was when she went swimming with the ball that Ookie had the most fun. Like all walruses, she enjoyed swimming on her back. That left her front flippers free to hold the

ball. Lazily and slowly, just floating or paddling a little, she swam back and forth across her pool, and the white ball was always with her. Sometimes she clasped it on her stomach or under her chin, or even balanced it on her whiskers, while she swam at full speed or coasted across the pool. Baby walruses probably play that way with pieces of ice when they are swimming with their mothers off the coast of Alaska, but a slick, round ball is harder to balance on your nose than a rough piece of ice.

Ookie almost never let the ball fall when she was swimming with it, but now and then it got away from her by accident. She liked to roll over and swim with the ball tucked under her chin, and usually, when she did that, the ball would suddenly escape and pop high into the air. If it popped high enough, it might fall over the outside wall of her pool. Then Ookie would begin to cry. "Ook-ook-ook-ook." That always brought a keeper running to see what was the matter, but as soon as he tossed the ball back to her she was happy again.

When she grew tired of swimming with the ball, Ookie invented another game. That was to see how high she could spit. Her best record was pretty high — nearly four feet.

Swimming along on her back, with the ball floating alongside, she would suddenly duck her head and take a big mouthful of water. And then — whoosh! She'd spray it high in the air. Visitors to the Aquarium always laughed when she did that, and stepped back from the wall so as not to get wet. But Ookie

wasn't trying to spit water on them — she was just doing it for fun — and if the water fell back on her own face, that was so much the better. Indeed, she liked to have Charley turn on the hose full force, so she could swim under the stream and let the water splatter on her face.

Many times during Ookie's babyhood summer she played so

hard and so long that at the end of the day she was tired. When all her friends had gone away and there were no visitors to amuse, she swam back to her little beach with her ball and leaned against the wall, just as if she was too tired to go to bed.

Of course, if some late visitors happened to come along just then, Ookie was likely to slide back into the water and start playing again, for she was just enough of a baby to like being a show-off!

But mostly, when evening came, Ookie was content to go

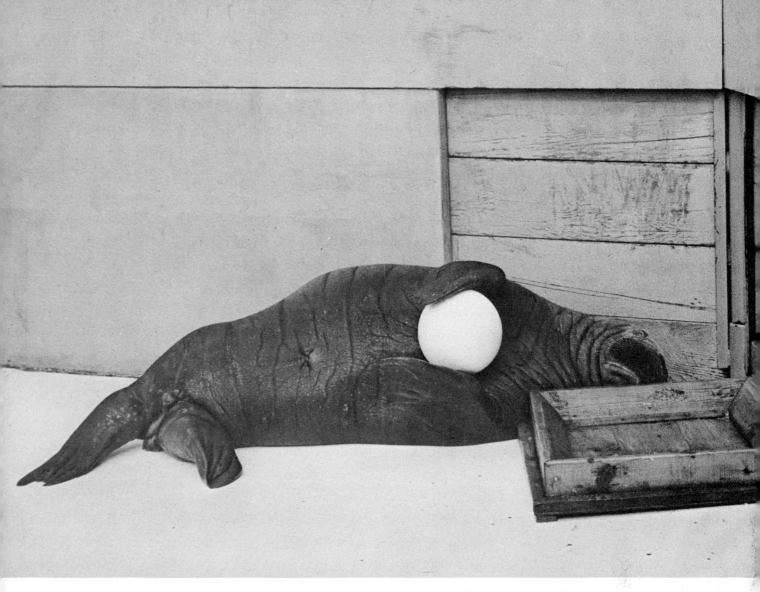

to sleep on her haul-out, with her favorite ball clasped in her flippers.

Late in the summer something wonderful happened to Ookie. The people at the Aquarium finally decided to put her into the pool with the harbor seals. They knew that Ookie wasn't really very lonely now. She had the ball to play with, and she had learned to spit streams of water, so that people stopped to laugh and talk to her, and she had Charley, her favorite keeper, to play with her many times a day. But still they knew that Ookie would have fun with other animals, and so one day they took down the gate between her pool and the seals' pool. Ookie flopped and hunched herself across the cement platform and dived into the water with the seals.

The seals were bigger now, and they weren't afraid of her any longer. There were two of them, and they both swam toward Ookie to make sure she was as friendly as they were. Maybe Ookie was afraid the Aquarium people would make her go back into her own pool if she paid any attention to the seals. At any rate, she didn't try to chase them. She just swam slowly around and around, and paid no attention when they swam up to look at her. But after a while she turned over on her back (the way walruses like to do) and began to swim *very* slowly. Then one of the little seals wriggled through the water right up to Ookie's side, scrambled up on her stomach and lay there, while Ookie went on swimming!

Ookie was about five times bigger than the seal, and she didn't mind if the little thing wanted to ride around the pool on her stomach. It was rather like having the ball to play with, although she didn't have to hold this one. Ookie was as happy and contented with the seals as if she had played with them all her life. When the seal finally slipped off into the water and swam up to her head to rub against her whiskers, Ookie held very still, the way she would have if Charley had been playing with her.

Before the summer was over, Ookie and one of the seals had become fast friends. Almost every day Ookie was allowed to go into the seal pool for a few hours, and as soon as she dived into the water the seal came over and rubbed against her whiskers. Then Ookie slowly started to swim, usually on her

back, and for a while the friendly seal swam alongside her.

Finally Ookie would hold out one of her big flippers, almost as large as the seal's whole body, and the little animal snuggled up to her and let himself be held firmly by her flipper. Together, with their eyes closed, they swam around and around and around the pool.

That was one of the happiest times of Ookie's life.

Then Ookie learned a trick. It wasn't much of a trick. Walruses are not like puppies or kittens or lots of other animals that can learn tricks easily and can be taught to do them when you say "Roll over" or "Sit up" or something like that. After

all, a walrus has a very heavy, thick body, and while its front flippers and hind flippers can be moved forward and backward and up and down, they aren't quite as useful as arms and legs. So there aren't many kinds of tricks that a walrus *can* do, even if it wants to.

Ookie's trick was to "shake hands" with her keeper's foot, and she learned to do it by accident.

Every day Charley brought her a special lunch of cut-up pieces of clam. But first he played with Ookie a little. He pushed against her whiskers until she opened her mouth. She was always willing to do this, for she knew Charley was going to drop a handful of clams into it. If he happened to move his hand a little to the side of her head, she rolled over until one of her front flippers was in the air.

One day, while she was doing this, Charley almost lost his balance, and started to fall. His foot came up under Ookie's flipper and that stopped him from falling. So the next day when he started to feed her, Ookie put out her flipper and held it on Charley's foot. When he moved his foot up and down, she held her flipper on it lightly as if she were shaking hands. Other times Charley reached down, took hold of Ookie's flipper, and shook it with his hand. If he forgot, she brushed his knee with her flipper until he remembered.

She liked shaking hands. Maybe it was her way of saying "Thank you" after Charley had given her the clams for lunch. Of course, it wasn't much of a trick. But it was one that Ookie had invented herself, and so everyone at the Aquarium liked it, too.

Ookie and Charley got to be great friends. The seals were fun for her, of course, and she liked swimming with them. She also liked playing with her ball and spitting water. But whenever her special friend Charley came to her pool to clean it with his scrubbing brush, Ookie stopped whatever she was doing and came over to help him. Most of the time Charley could have cleaned the pool a great deal faster if Ookie had let him alone, but Charley liked Ookie as much as she liked him, so he always found time to play with her.

When he scrubbed the cement floor at the edge of the pool, Charley had to dip his brush in the water many times, and it was great fun for Ookie to swim over and seize the brush in her flippers. Sometimes she managed to pull the scrubbing part of the brush off the handle, and then Charley was in trouble! For Ookie usually carried the brush in her mouth down under the water, where she pushed it around the bottom as if she were scrubbing the floor of the pool. Charley would have to get a very long pole and try to get the brush away from her. If she was feeling especially playful, it might take most of the morning to get the brush back.

But most of the time Ookie just swam up and took hold of the brush, and waited until Charley began to scrub her with it. She liked that, because it was a heavy, coarse brush that scratched her thick skin and made her feel good. She would

throw back her head and just stand there in the water while Charley scrubbed away at her front flippers and chest.

If Charley had plenty of time, he first scrubbed Ookie while she was in the water and then backed away until she had room to come out. If he didn't back away when she thought he should, she heaved herself out of the water and tumbled all over his feet and legs.

But when Charley had plenty of time, Ookie knew that she was going to get a good scrubbing. She would flop out of the water and lie on the cement, and Charley would push the brush up and down her back. The harder he scrubbed, the better Ookie liked it. Her dark-brown hair glistened and sparkled, and Charley was always careful at the end to rub it down smooth with his brush.

Ookie liked to be scrubbed all over, so after Charley had scrubbed her back she always rolled over and pretended to go to sleep while he rubbed the brush up and down on her stomach. That was sheer bliss! Ookie would have let Charley scrub her all morning if he'd had time to do it.

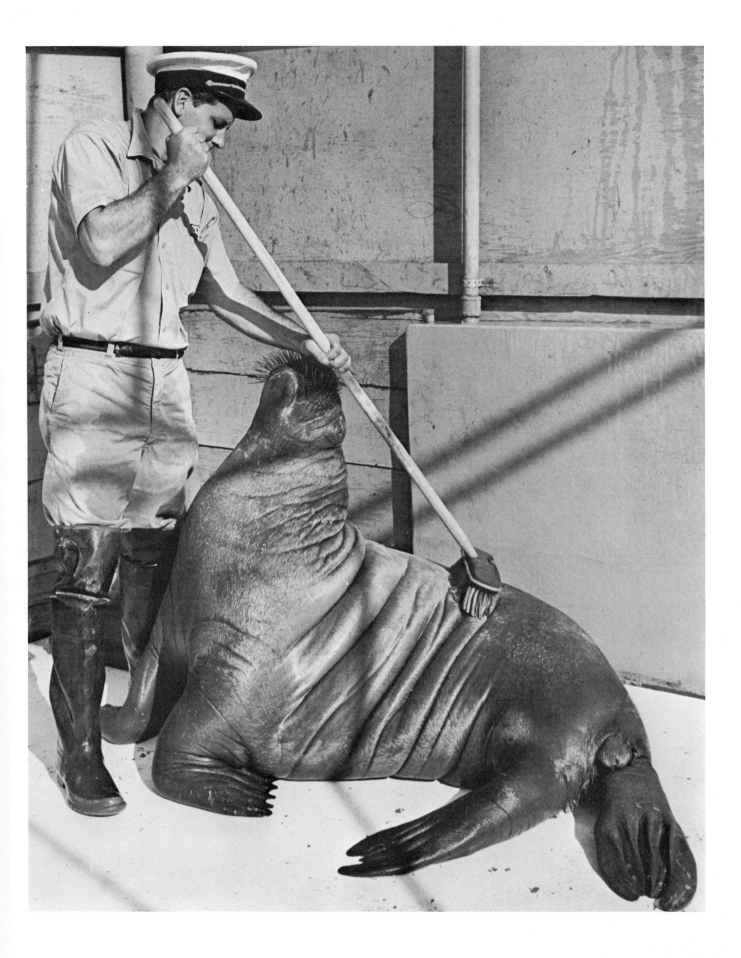

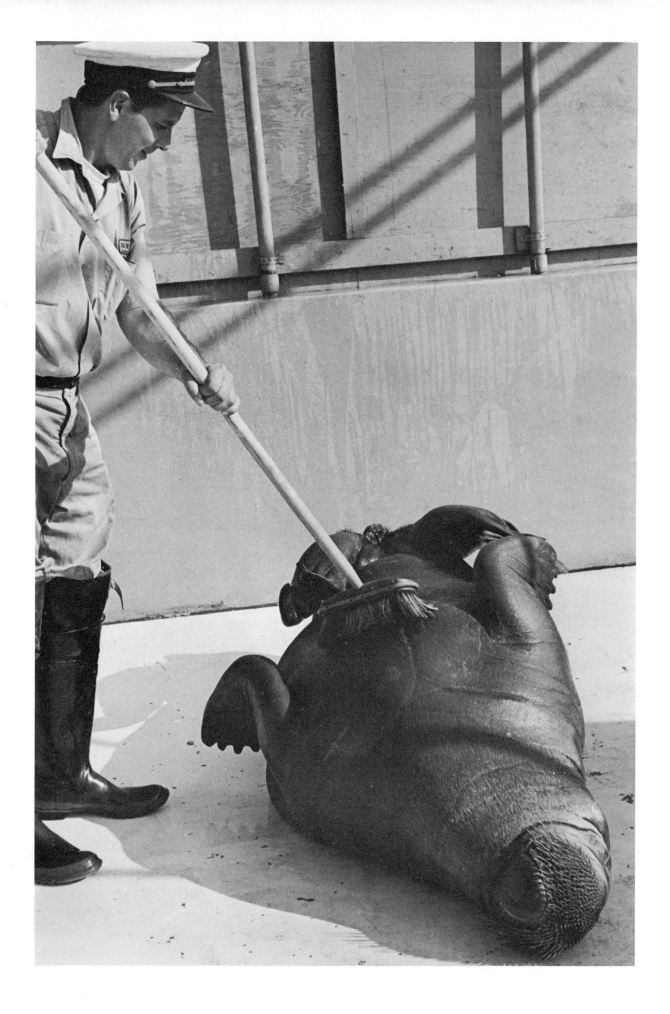

At the very end, after Charley had scrubbed her until he was tired, Ookie said "Thank you!" in her own way. She sat up and, when Charley put his head down, gently rubbed his face with her whiskers.

They were pretty scratchy whiskers, and Charley said it was almost like having his chin rubbed with the scrubbing brush, but since that was Ookie's way of showing how much she liked her keeper, he let her do it.

All that summer the nicest things kept happening to Ookie! At least she thought they were nice. Once a man leaned over the wall of her pool to pet her, and his glasses fell off his nose into the water. Nobody had ever given her glasses to play with before, and they made a very interesting new toy. Ookie pushed them all around the floor of the pool with her nose. Then she pushed them around the cement wall, until she got tired of playing with them and let her friend Charley take them out of her mouth and give them back to the man. Rubbing the glasses on the cement floor and wall scratched them rather badly, so that the man couldn't see through them any more. But Ookie seemed to think he had dropped them just for her pleasure, and as long as he stood around the edge of the pool she kept following him and waiting for him to drop them again.

Another time a little boy sat on the edge of her pool. Ookie swam over very fast, leaped out of the water, and bumped the boy where he stuck out behind. That made him fall off the wall, and everybody laughed. Ookie would have liked to bump somebody else, and she kept swimming around, looking for the opportunity, but nobody wanted to play that game with her.

Besides all these nice things, Charley came to see her every day. He always said, "Hi, Ookie! How's the girl today?" or "Hi, Ookie! You sure are getting fat," and Ookie always said "Ook-ook-ook" right back at him.

Charley always came to see Ookie at the same time every morning. She had no way of telling time, of course, but she had a pretty good way of knowing when to expect Charley to climb over the wall and pat her whiskers. It was just about the time each morning when she had almost forgotten breakfast and was beginning to think about lunch.

One day Charley didn't climb over her wall when he was supposed to. In fact, it was quite a long time before any keeper came to see her, and even then it wasn't her good friend Charley — it was someone she had never seen before.

Ookie liked the new keeper all right, for she liked anybody who would talk to her and bring her food, but the new keeper was in a hurry, and he just dumped the fish and clams in the corner and climbed out of the pool again.

Where was Charley?

Now maybe walruses can't learn tricks like some other animals, and maybe they can't make many sounds, except "Ook-ook-ook," but they have pretty good eyes, and they can hear quite well. And Ookie could hear Charley's voice. He was in the next pool, around the corner of the wall.

He was talking to another animal.

Very softly, very quietly, Ookie dragged herself over to the corner of her pool and stood up on her hind flippers to look around the edge of the wall. Then she saw something awful.

Her friend Charley was giving a bottle of formula to *another* walrus! A baby walrus. He had his back to Ookie, and he was talking to the baby just the way he used to talk to her.